Sing 15 Showtunes!

Wise Publications
part of The Music Sales Group
London/New York/Paris/Sydney/Copenhagen/Berlin/Madrid/Tokyo

Published by
Wise Publications
8/9 Frith Street, London, W1D 3JB, England.

Exclusive distributors:
Music Sales Limited
Distribution Centre, Newmarket Road,
Bury St Edmunds, Suffolk, IP33 3YB, England.
Music Sales Pty Limited
120 Rothschild Avenue, Rosebery, NSW 2018, Australia.

Order No. AM978956
ISBN 1-84449-308-3
This book © Copyright 2004 by Wise Publications.

Compiled by Lucy Holliday.
Music processed by Paul Ewers Music Design.
Cover photograph by James Bareham
(Zehra Naqvi and Stephen Rahman Hughes from
the London production of *Bombay Dreams*).

Printed in the United Kingdom by Printwise (Haverhill) Limited, Haverhill, Suffolk.

www.musicsales.com

As Long As He Needs Me

Words & Music by Lionel Bart

♩ = 84 **Slowly**

As long as he needs

me,_____ oh yes he does need me,_____ in spite of

what you see,_____ I'm sure that he needs

me. Who else would love him still,_____ when they've been

used so ill?_____ He knows I al - ways will,_____ as long as

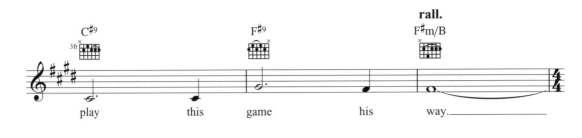

rall.

play this game his way._____

a tempo

_____ As long as he needs me,_____ I know where

I must be,_____ I'll cling on stead - fast -

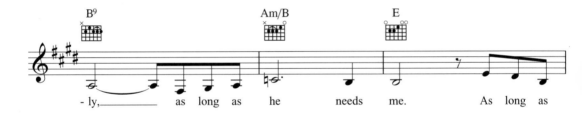

- ly,_____ as long as he needs me. As long as

poco più mosso

life is long,_____ I'll love him right or

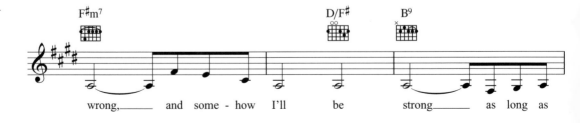

wrong,_____ and some - how I'll be strong_____ as long as

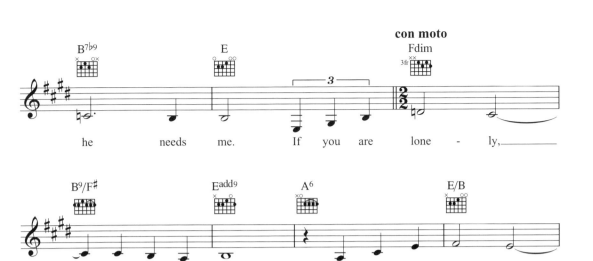

con moto

he needs me. If you are lone - ly,_____

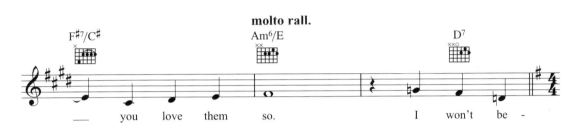

_____ then you will know when some - one needs you,_____

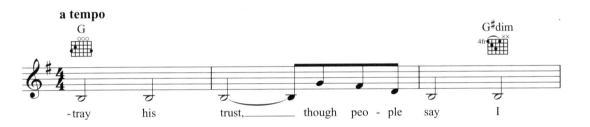

molto rall.

_____ you love them so. I won't be -

a tempo

- tray his trust,_____ though peo - ple say I

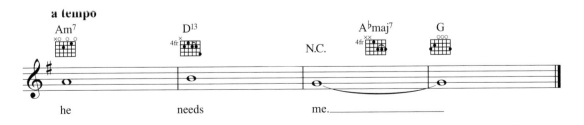

rall.

must,_____ I've got to stay true, just_____ as long as

a tempo

N.C.

he needs me._____

7

Cabaret

Words by Fred Ebb
Music by John Kander

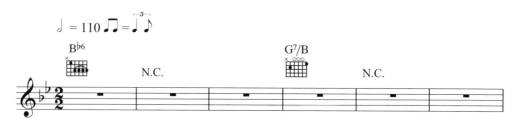

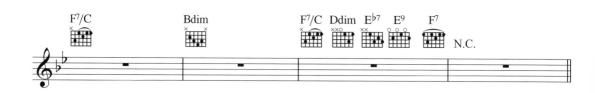

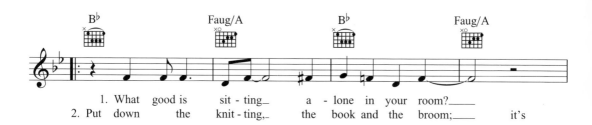

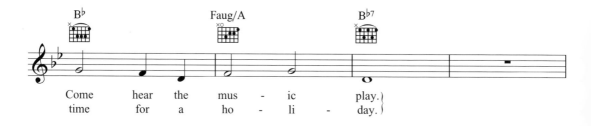

1. What good is sit-ting__ a - lone in your room?_____
2. Put down the knit-ting,__ the book and the broom;_____ it's

Come hear the mus - ic play.)
time for a ho - li - day.)

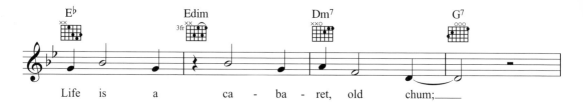

Life is a ca - ba - ret, old chum;_____

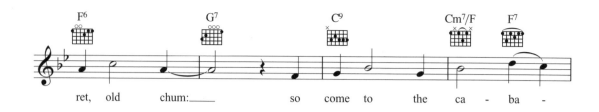

ret, old chum:____ so come to the ca - ba -

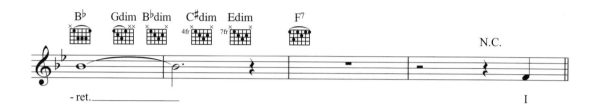

N.C.

- ret._____ I

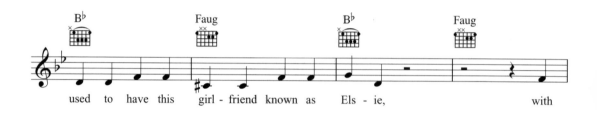

used to have this girl - friend known as Els - ie, with

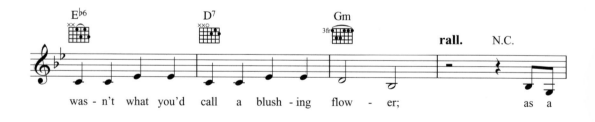

whom I shared four sor - did rooms in Chel - sea. She

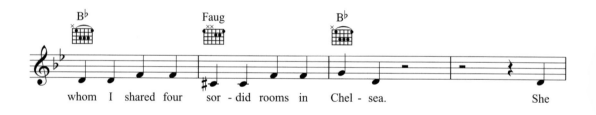

rall. N.C.

was - n't what you'd call a blush - ing flow - er; as a

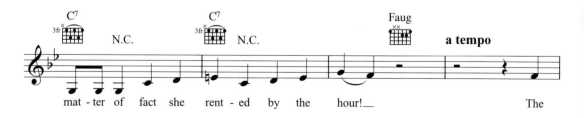

a tempo

mat - ter of fact she rent - ed by the hour!__ The

10

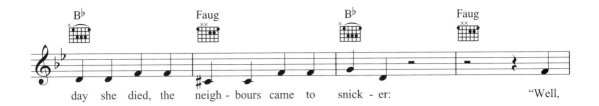

day she died, the neigh - bours came to snick - er: "Well,

slower, free time

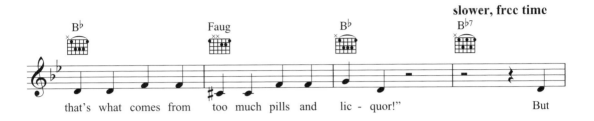

that's what comes from too much pills and lic - quor!" But

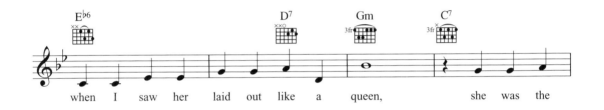

when I saw her laid out like a queen, she was the

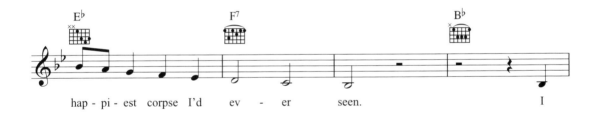

hap - pi - est corpse I'd ev - er seen. I

think of Els - ie to this ve - ry day. I re -

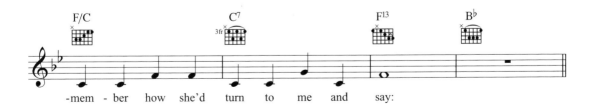

-mem - ber how she'd turn to me and say:

"What good is sit - ting all a - lone in your room?

Come hear the mu - sic play.

Life is a ca - ba - ret, old chum;

in rhythm, accel.

come to the ca - ba - ret." And as for

a tempo   **much slower**

me hah! And as for me, I made my mind up

back in Chel - sea, when I go I'm go -ing like Els - ie.

in rhythm, accel.

Start by ad - mit - ting, from crad - le to tomb,_____ it

is - n't that - a long a stay._____

Life is a ca - ba - ret, old chum;_____ it's on - ly a_____

_____ ca - ba - ret, old chum;_____ and I love a ca -

- ba - - ret._____

Don't Cry For Me Argentina

Words by Tim Rice
Music by Andrew Lloyd Webber

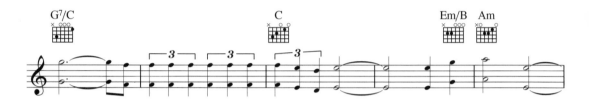

(instrumental)

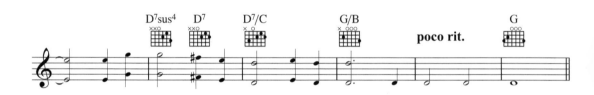

poco rit.

1. It won't be ea-sy, you'll think it strange, when I

try to ex-plain how I feel, that I still need your love af-ter all that I've done:___

You won't be - lieve me, all you will see is a girl you once knew, al-

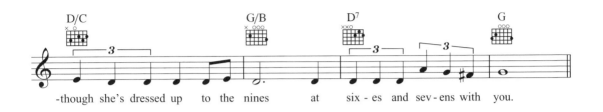

-though she's dressed up to the nines at six - es and sev - ens with you.

2. I had to let it hap - pen, I had to change; Could-n't

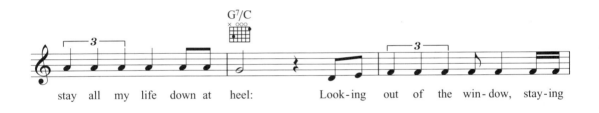

stay all my life down at heel: Look - ing out of the win - dow, stay - ing

out of the sun. So I chose free - dom,

run - ning a - round try - ing ev - 'ry - thing new; but no - thing im - pressed me at

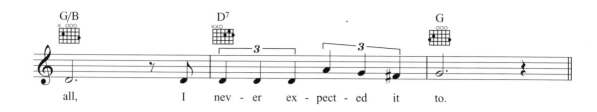

all, I nev - er ex - pect - ed it to.

Don't cry for me Ar - gen - ti - na,_____ the truth is I nev - er

left you; All through my wild days, my mad ex - ist - ence, I kept my

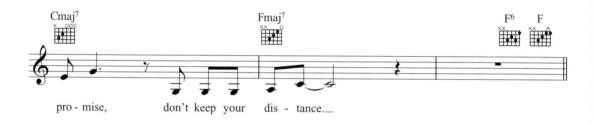

pro - mise, don't keep your dis - tance._

3. And as for for - tune and as for fame, I

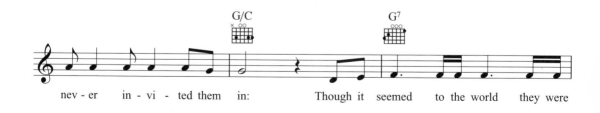

nev - er in - vi - ted them in: Though it seemed to the world they were

all I de - sired. They are il - lu - sions,__ they're

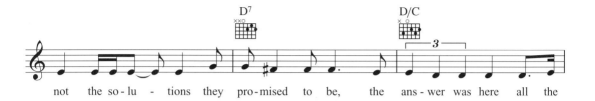

not the so - lu - tions they pro - mised to be, the ans - wer was here all the

time_____ I love you and hope you love me.

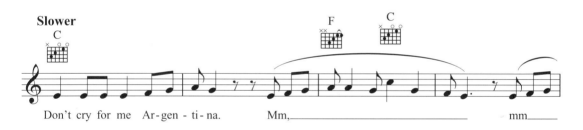

Slower

Don't cry for me Ar - gen - ti - na. Mm,_____ mm___

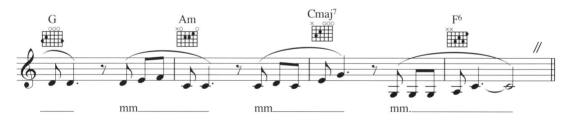

_____ mm_____ mm___ mm.___

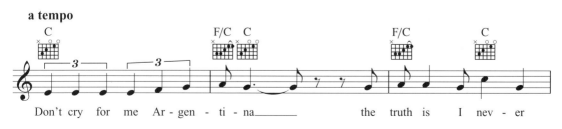

a tempo

Don't cry for me Ar - gen - ti - na_____ the truth is I nev - er

17

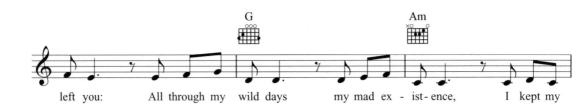

left you: All through my wild days my mad ex - ist - ence, I kept my

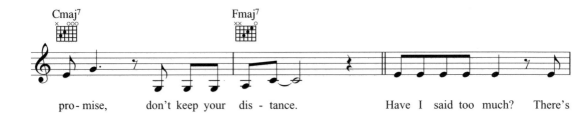

pro - mise, don't keep your dis - tance. Have I said too much? There's

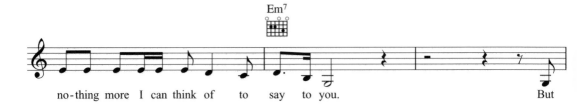

no - thing more I can think of to say to you. But

all you have to do is look at me to know that ev - 'ry word is true.

(instrumental)

Hopelessly Devoted To You

Words & Music by John Farrar

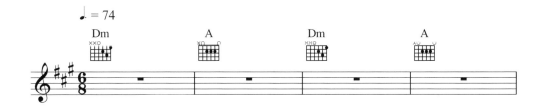

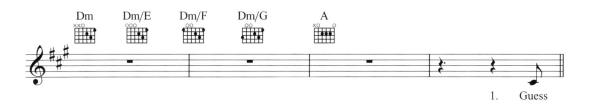

1. Guess

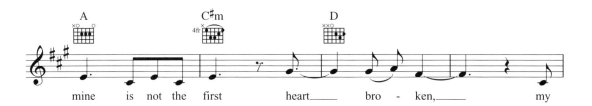

mine is not the first heart_____ bro - ken,_____ my

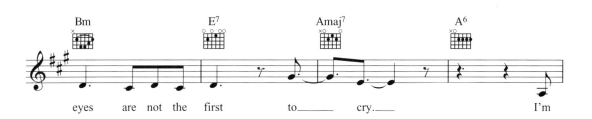

eyes are not the first to_____ cry._____ I'm

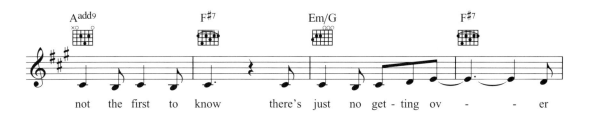

not the first to know there's just no get - ting ov - - er

you.

2. I

know   I'm   just   a   fool   who's____   will - ing____   to
(3.)head   is   say - ing   "Fool,   for - get   him."____   My

sit   a - round____   and   wait   for   you.   But
heart   is   say - ing   "Don't   let   go."

ba - by, can't   you   see   there's   no - thing   else   for   me____   to
Hold   on   to   the   end,   and   that's   what   I   in - tend____   to

do.____   I'm   hope - less - ly   de - vot - ed____   to
do.____

you.   But   now   there's

no - where to hide   since you pushed my love a - side.___   I'm___

___ out___ of my head,   hope - less - ly   de - vo - ted___   to

you.___   Hope - less - ly   de - vo - ted___   to

you.___   Hope - less - ly   de -

1.
-vo - ted___   to   you.___

2.
3. My   - vot - ed___   to   you.___   Ooh.

I Don't Know How To Love Him

Words by Tim Rice
Music by Andrew Lloyd Webber

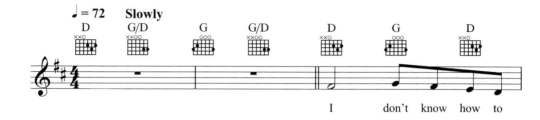

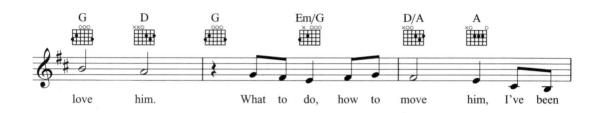

I   don't know how to love   him.   What to do, how to move   him, I've been

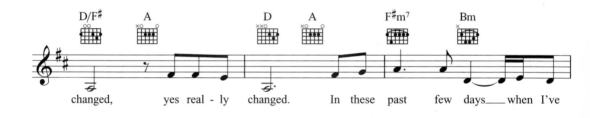

changed,   yes real - ly changed.   In these past few days____ when I've

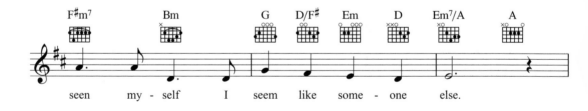

seen   my - self   I   seem   like some - one   else.

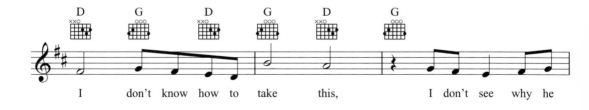

I   don't know how to take   this,   I don't see why he

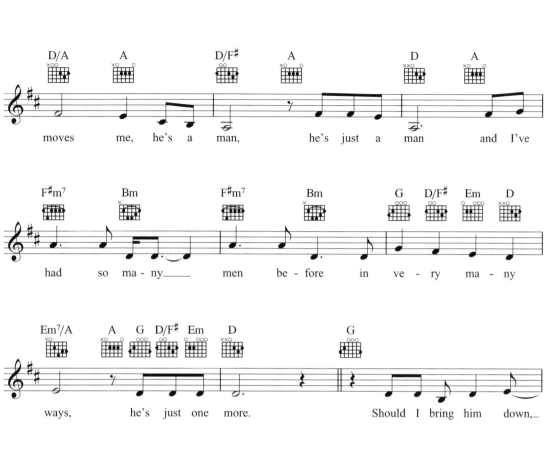

moves me, he's a man, he's just a man and I've

had so ma-ny_____ men be-fore in ve-ry ma-ny

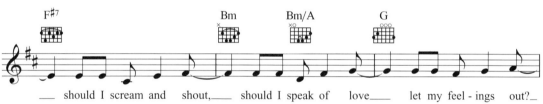

ways, he's just one more. Should I bring him down,_

should I scream and shout,_ should I speak of love_____ let my feel-ings out?_

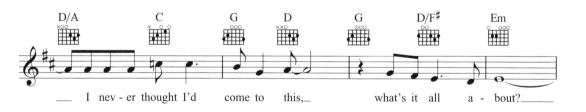

_ I nev-er thought I'd come to this,_ what's it all a-bout?_____

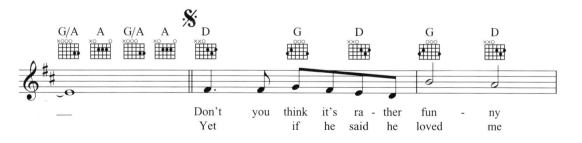

Don't you think it's ra-ther fun - ny
Yet if he said he loved me

I should be in this po - si - tion? I'm the
I'd be lost, I'd be fright - ened. I could - n't

one who's al - ways been so calm, so cool, no lov - er's fool,
cope, just could - n't cope, I'd turn my head, I'd back a - way I

To Coda ⊕

run - ning ev - 'ry show. He scares me so. *(instrumental)*
would - n't want to know. He scares me so.

I nev - er thought I'd

D.S. al Coda

come to this,__ what's it all a - bout?__

⊕ *Coda*

so. I want him so, I love him so.

My Favourite Things

Words by Oscar Hammerstein II
Music by Richard Rodgers

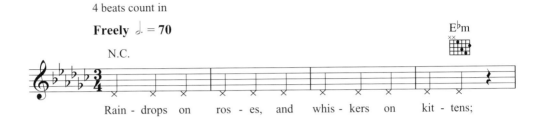

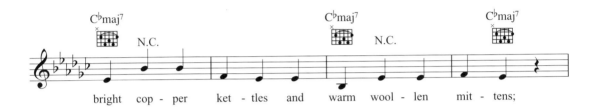

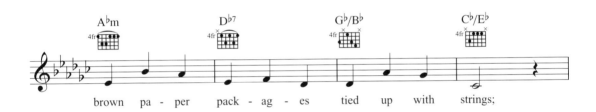

Cream col - oured pon - ies and crisp ap - ple stru - dels;

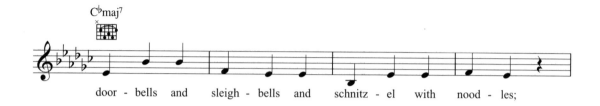

door - bells and sleigh - bells and schnitz - el with nood - les;

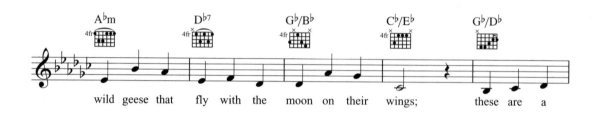

wild geese that fly with the moon on their wings; these are a

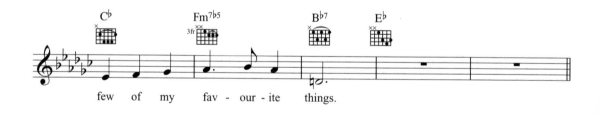

few of my fav - our - ite things.

Girls in white dress - es with blue sat - in sash - es;

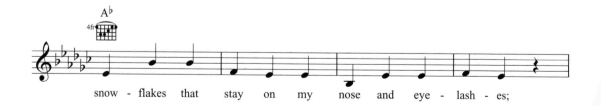

snow - flakes that stay on my nose and eye - lash - es;

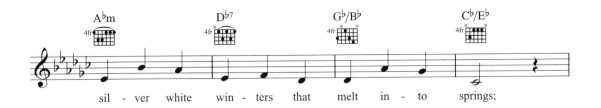

sil - ver white win - ters that melt in - to springs;

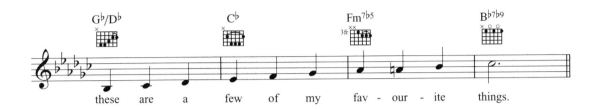

these are a few of my fav - our - ite things.

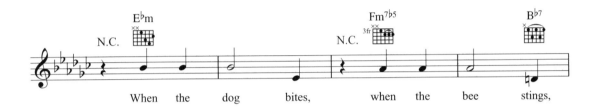

When the dog bites, when the bee stings,

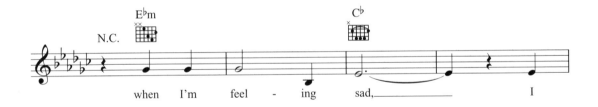

when I'm feel - ing sad,_____ I

sim - ply re - mem - ber my fav - our - ite things, and

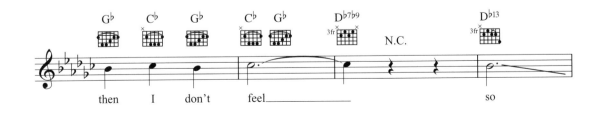

then I don't feel_____ so

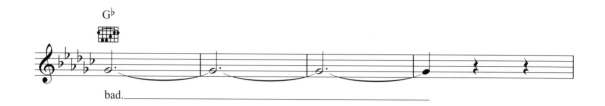

bad.

Rain - drops on ros - es and whisk - ers on kit - tens;

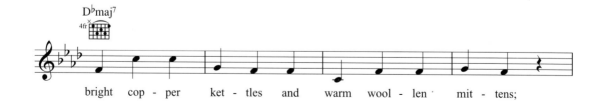

bright cop - per ket - tles and warm wool - len mit - tens;

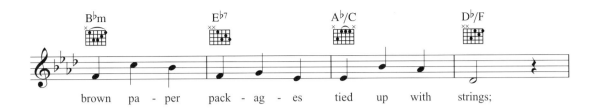

brown pa - per pack - ag - es tied up with strings;

these are a few of my fav - our - ite things.

Cream col - oured pon - ies and crisp ap - ple strud - els;

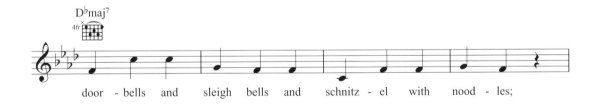

door - bells and sleigh bells and schnitz - el with nood - les;

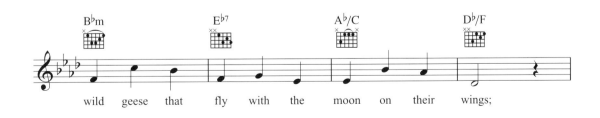

wild geese that fly with the moon on their wings;

these are a few of my fav - our - ite things.

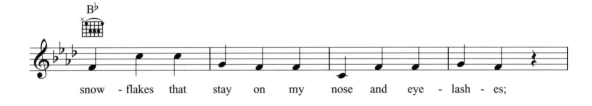

Girls in white dress - es with blue sat - in sash - es;

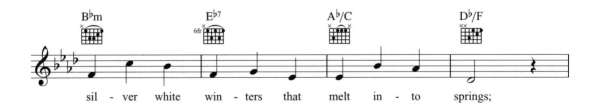

snow - flakes that stay on my nose and eye - lash - es;

sil - ver white win - ters that melt in - to springs;

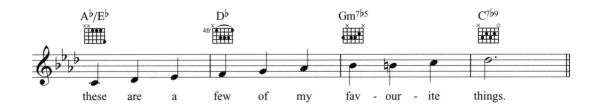

these are a few of my fav - our - ite things.

When the dog bites, when the bee stings,

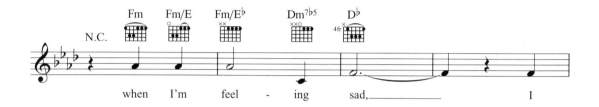

when I'm feel - ing sad,_____ I

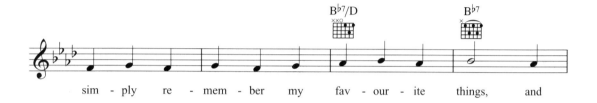

sim - ply re - mem - ber my fav - our - ite things, and

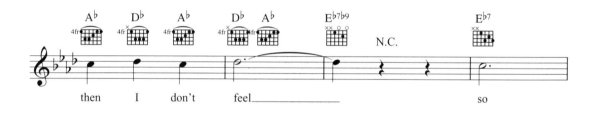

then I don't feel_____ so

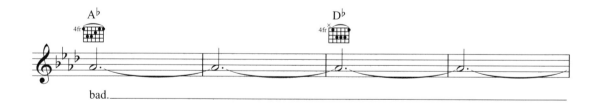

bad._____

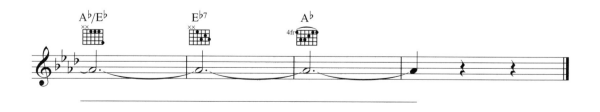

Memory

Words by Trevor Nunn after T.S. Eliot
Music by Andrew Lloyd Webber

Ev - 'ry street lamp seems to beat a fa - tal - is - tic warn - ing. Some - one mut - ters and a street lamp gut - ters and soon it will be morn - ing.

a tempo

Day - light. I must wait for the sun - rise, I must think of a new life and I must-n't give in. When the dawn comes to - night will be a me - mo - ry too and a

new day _____ will _____ be - gin.

(strings)

poco più mosso

Burnt out ends of smo - ky days, _____ the stale cold smell ___ of

morn - ing. _____ The street lamp dies an - oth - er

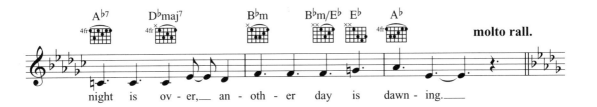

molto rall.

night is ov - er,___ an - oth - er day is dawn - ing.___

meno mosso

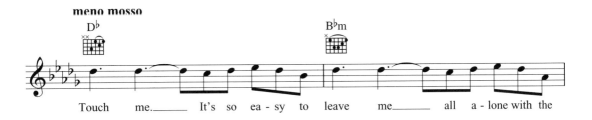

Touch me.___ It's so ea - sy to leave me___ all a - lone with the

mem - 'ry___ of my days in the sun.___ If you

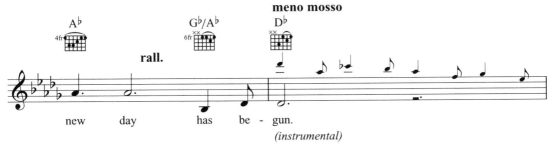

touch me you'll un - der - stand what hap - pi - ness is. Look a

meno mosso

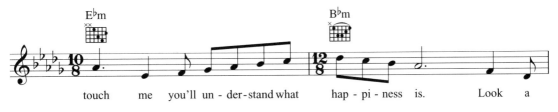

rall.

new day has be - gun.

(instrumental)

rall.

Now That I've Seen Her (Her Or Me)
(from "Miss Saigon")

Words by Alain Boublil & Richard Maltby Jr.
Music by Claude-Michel Schönberg

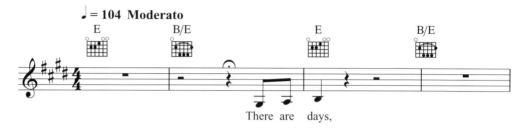

There are days,

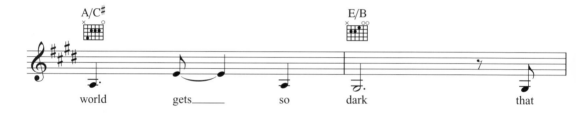

there are days when your life clouds ov - er, and the

world gets____ so dark that

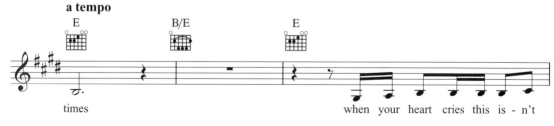

all at once you can't tell night from day. There are

times when your heart cries this is - n't

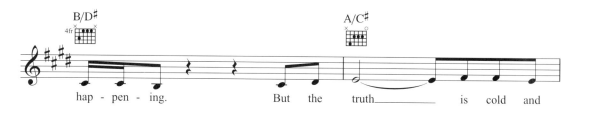

hap - pen - ing. But the truth_____ is cold and

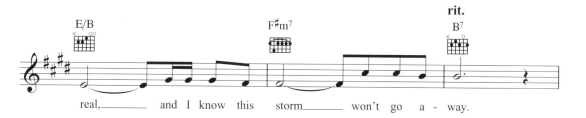

real,_____ and I know this storm_____ won't go a - way.

a tempo

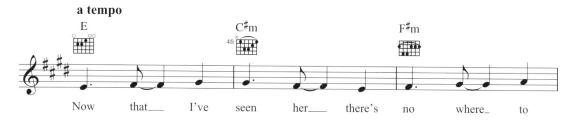

Now that____ I've seen her____ there's no where_ to

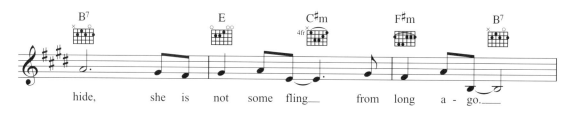

hide, she is not some fling____ from long a - go.____

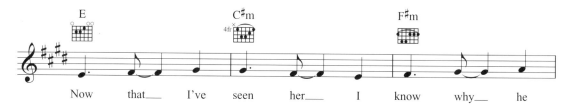

Now that____ I've seen her____ I know why____ he

lied, and I think it was bet - ter when I did - n't

know._____ In her

eyes, in her voice,

poco più mosso

in the heat_____ that filled the air part of

him_____ still lin-gers there. I know what pain her life to-

-day must be. But if it all comes down to

rall.

her or me, I won't wait, I_____ swear_____ I'll

a tempo

fight.

Now that__ I've seen her__ she's more than__ a

name, she is not some fling__ from long a - go.__

rall.

Now that__ I've seen her__ I can't stay__ the

same. Who's the man that I al - ways trust - ed.

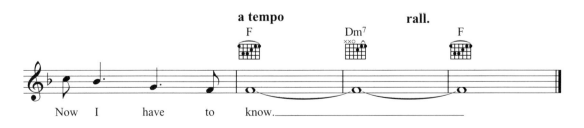

a tempo   rall.

Now I have to know.__

On My Own
(from "Les Misérables")

Words by Alain Boublil & Jean-Marc Natel
Music by Claude-Michel Schönberg

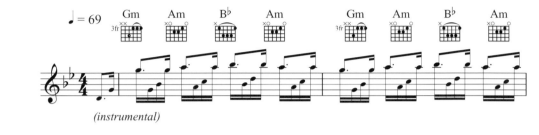

(instrumental)

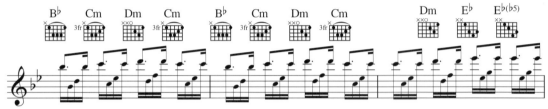

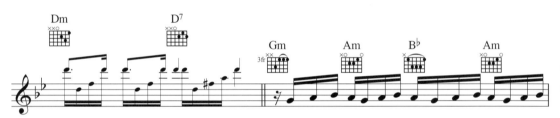

And now I'm all a-lone a-gain; no where to go, no one to

turn to.   I did not want your mo - ney, sir, I came out here 'cause I was

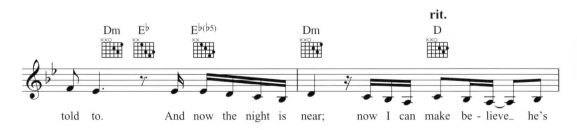

told to.   And now the night is near;   now I can make be - lieve_ he's

40

a tempo

here.

Some-times I walk a - lone at night, when ev -'ry - bo - dy else is

sleep - ing.

I think of him and then I'm hap - py with the com - pa - ny I'm

rit.

keep - ing.

The ci - ty goes to bed, and I can live in - side_ my

♩ = **72 a tempo**

head.

On my own, pre - tend - ing he's be -

rain, the pave - ment shines like

-side_ me._ All a - lone, I walk with him till morn - ing. With - out

sil - ver._ All the lights are mis - ty in the ri - ver. In the

him, I feel his arms a - round me. And

dark - ness, the trees are full of star - light. And

when I lose my way I close my eyes and he has found me! In the
all I see is him and me for ev - er and for ev - er. And I

know it's on - ly in my mind, that I'm talk - ing to my - self and not to

him. And, al - though I know that he is blind, still I

say there's a way for_____ us. I

love him_____ but when the night is ov - er,_____ he is

gone, the ri - ver's just a ri - ver. With - out him, the world a - round me

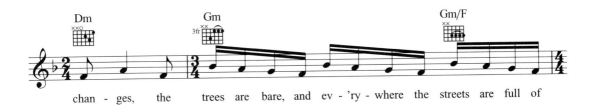

chan - ges, the trees are bare, and ev -'ry-where the streets are full of

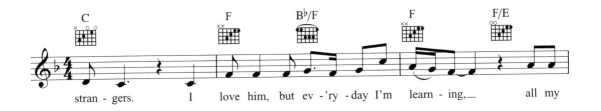

stran - gers. I love him, but ev -'ry -day I'm learn - ing,— all my

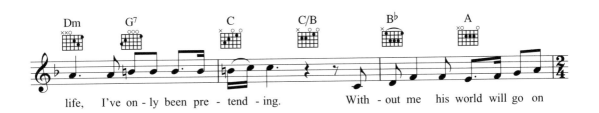

life, I've on -ly been pre -tend -ing. With - out me his world will go on

turn - ing. A world that's full of hap -pi -ness that I have nev - er

known. I love him, I love him, I

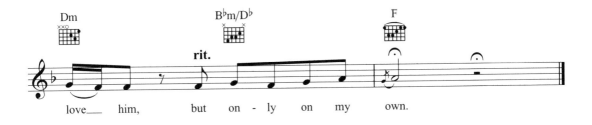

love— him, but on -ly on my own.

Shakalaka Baby

Words & Music by A. R. Rahman,
Don Black & Marius De Vries

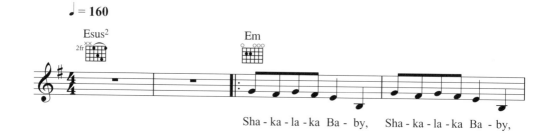

Sha - ka - la - ka Ba - by, Sha - ka - la - ka Ba - by,

mm._____ 1. Saw your face, and the dam-age was done;_

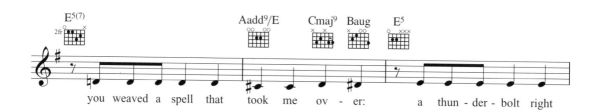

you weaved a spell that took me ov - er: a thun - der - bolt right

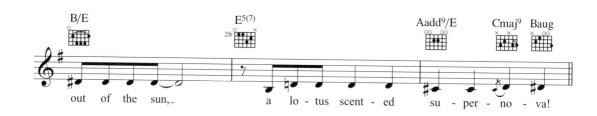

out of the sun,_ a lo - tus scent - ed su - per - no - va!

2. Catch the rhy - thm, jump to the beat;_ the nights are warm and my
3. In a trance go - ing out of my mind, you made a flame that__

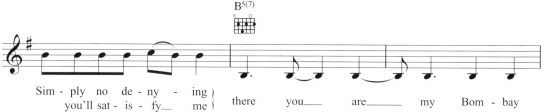

be.   Sha-ka-la-ka ba-by,   sha-ka-la-ka ba-by   come and sha-ka-la-ka with

me.   Sha-ka-la-ka ba-by,   sha-ka-la-ka ba-by,   no-thing here is ev-er what it
                                                                   I just want to love you ev-'ry
                                                                   no-thing here at all I need to

seems.   Sha-ka-la-ka ba-by,   sha-ka-la-ka ba-by,
day,   sha-ka-la-ka ba-by,   sha-ka-la-ka ba-by,
know,   sha-ka-la-ka ba-by,   sha-ka-la-ka ba-by,

To Coda ⊕   N.C.

let me take you with me in my dreams.   (No no no no no no no   no   no__ no no
prom-ise me you'll ne-ver go a-way.
now you're here I'll ne-ver let you

no no no no no no   no   no no__ no no.   No no no no no no

1. B⁷   2.
               N.C.

no   no__ no no   no no no no no no   no   no no no_ no no.

A se-cret moon and a   jas-mine breeze: pray we'll share ma-ny nights like these,

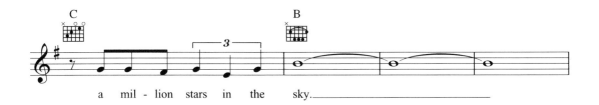

a mil - lion stars in the sky._____

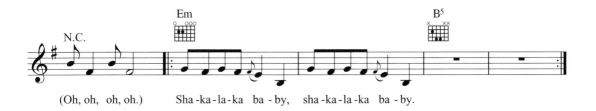

(Oh, oh, oh, oh.)   Sha -ka -la -ka ba - by,   sha -ka -la -ka ba - by.

Ad lib instrumental/vocal

Ik baa -ri phir jo aa - na   hrzy bin mil -ay phir kyo jaa - na   ai -sa

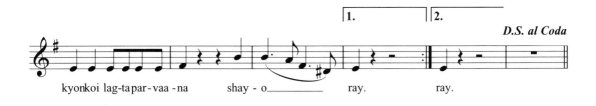

D.S. al Coda

kyonkoi lag-ta par -vaa -na   shay -o_____ ray.   ray.

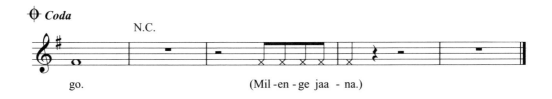

go.   (Mil -en -ge jaa - na.)

No One But You
(Only The Good Die Young)

Words & Music by Brian May

1. A hand above the water, an angel reaching for the sky: is it raining in Heaven?
2. Another tricky situation; I get to drowning in the blues. And I find myself thinking

Do you want us to cry? And ev'ry-where the brok-en heart-ed,
well, what would you do? Yes, it was such an op-er-a-tion,

on ev'ry lone-ly av-en-ue: no-one could reach them,
for-ev-er pay-ing ev-'ry due. Hell, you made a sen-sa-tion!

no one but you. One by one, on-ly the
So you found a way through! One by one, on-ly the

good die____ young. They're on-ly fly-ing too close_ to the sun; and life____ goes
good die____ young. They're on-ly fly-ing too close_ to the sun; and we'll____ re-

on____ with-out__ you.____
-mem - ber for - ev - er.____

3. And now the par - ty must be__ ov - er.__

I guess_we'll nev - er un - der - stand____ the sense of your leav-ing:

___ was it the way it was____ planned?__

And so we grace_ an - oth - er____ ta - ble,____

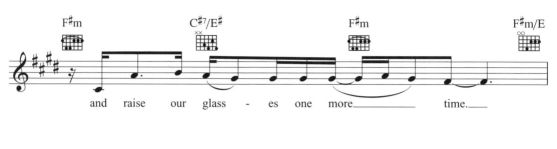

and raise our glass - es one more_____ time.____

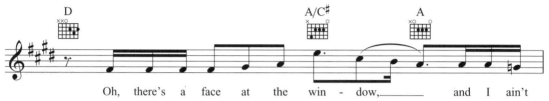

Oh, there's a face at the win - dow,_____ and I ain't

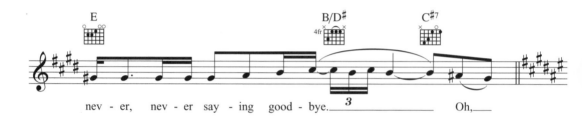

nev - er, nev - er say - ing good - bye.____ Oh,___

one by_____ one,_ on - ly the good___ die_____ young._ They're on - ly

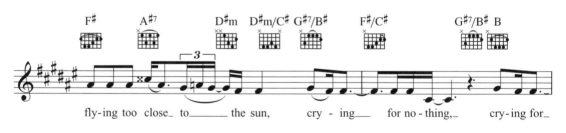

fly-ing too close_ to_____ the sun, cry - ing___ for no - thing,_ cry-ing for_

rit.   **molto rit.**   **a tempo**

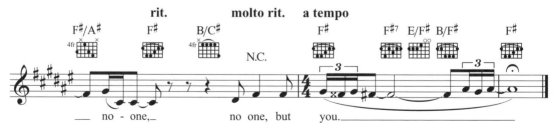

___ no - one,_ no one, but you._____

Tell Me It's Not True

Words & Music by Willy Russell

1. Tell me it's not true. Say it's just a sto - - ry.
2. Say it's just some clowns, two play - ers in the lime - - light,

Some - thing in the news.___ and bring the cur - tain down.___

Tell me it's not true, though it's here be - fore ___ me.
Say it's just two clowns who could - n't get their lines ___ right.

Say it's just a dream, say it's just a scene_____
Say it's just a show, on the ra-di-o,_____ that

from an old mo - vie of years_____ a -
we can turn ov - er and start_____ a -

- go; from an old mo - vie of
- gain; that_____ we can turn ov - er, it's

Ma - ri - lyn_____ Mon - roe.)
on - ly_____ a game.)

Tell me it's not true. Say I on - ly

dreamed_____ it. And morn - ing will come

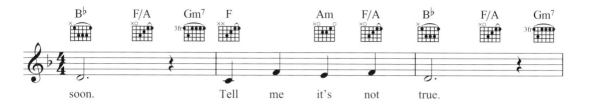

soon. Tell me it's not true.

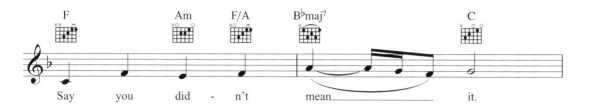

Say you did - n't mean_____ it.

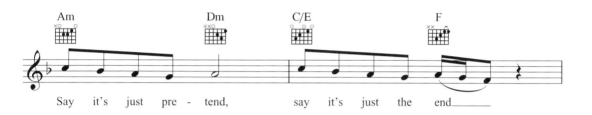

Say it's just pre - tend, say it's just the end_____

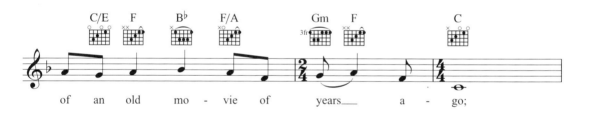

of an old mo - vie of years___ a - go;

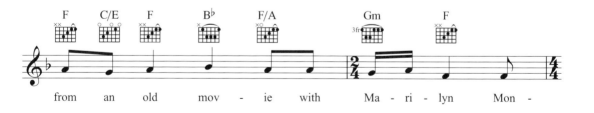

from an old mov - ie with Ma - ri - lyn Mon -

molto rall.

- roe._____

There Are Worse Things I Could Do

Words & Music by Jim Jacobs & Warren Casey

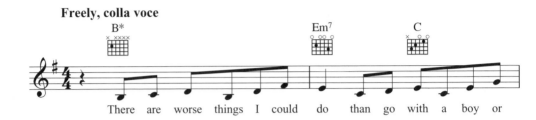

There are worse things I could do than go with a boy or

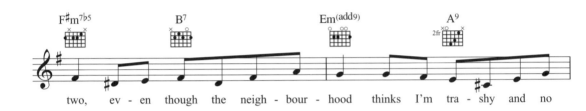

two, ev - en though the neigh - bour - hood thinks I'm tra - shy and no

good; I sup - pose it could be true, but there are worse things I could

do. I could flirt with_ all the guys,_

smile at them and_ bat my eyes,_

press a - gainst them___ when we dance,___ make them think they___ stand a

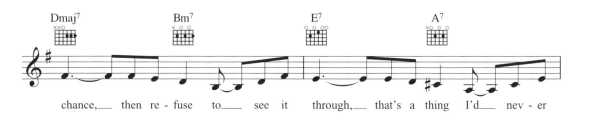

chance,___ then re - fuse to___ see it through,___ that's a thing I'd___ nev - er

do. I could stay home___ ev - 'ry night,_____

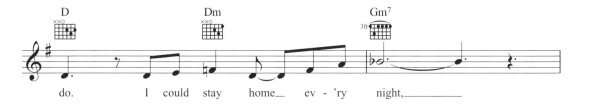

wait a - round for___ Mis - ter Right._____

Take cold show - ers___ ev - 'ry day,_____ and throw my___ life a -

- way_____ on a dream that___ won't come true._____

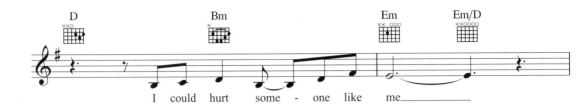

I could hurt some - one like me_____

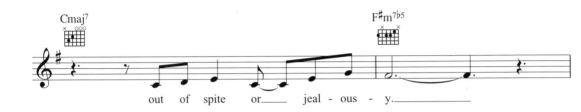

out of spite or_____ jeal - ous - y._____

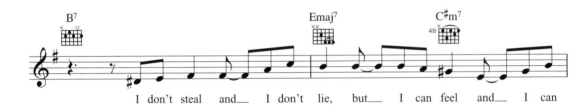

I don't steal and___ I don't lie, but___ I can feel and___ I can

cry: a fact I'll bet you___ nev - er knew._____

But to cry in___ front of you,_____ that's the worst thing_ I could

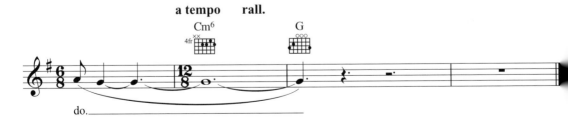

do._____

What I Did For Love

Words by Edward Kleban
Music by Marvin Hamlisch

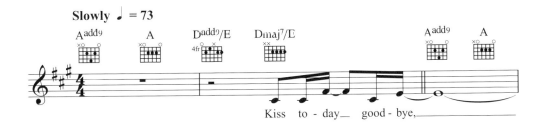

Kiss to-day__ good-bye,____

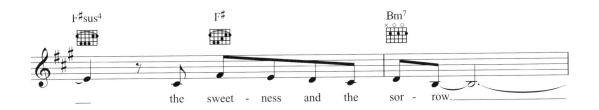

__ the sweet-ness and the sor-row.__

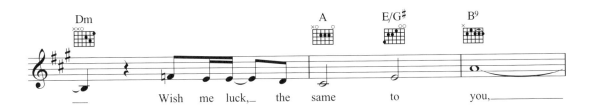

__ Wish me luck,__ the same to you,____

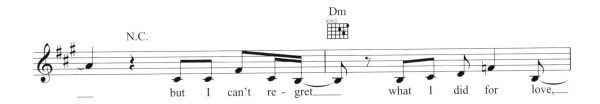

__ but I can't re-gret__ what I did for love,

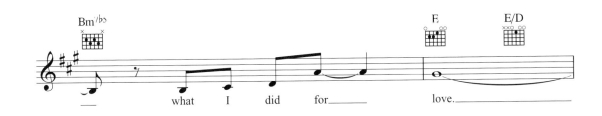

what I did for__ love.____

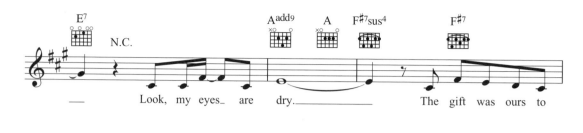

Look, my eyes are dry. The gift was ours to

bor - row. It's as if we al - ways

knew, and I won't for - get what I did for love.

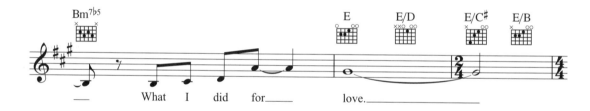

What I did for love.

Gone, love is nev - er gone.

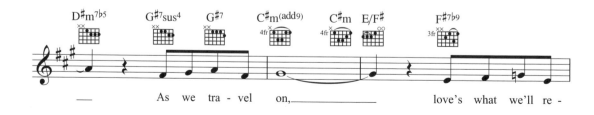

As we tra - vel on, love's what we'll re -

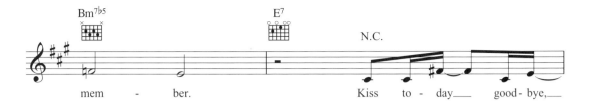

mem - ber. Kiss to - day___ good - bye,___

_____ and point me t'ward to - mor - row.___

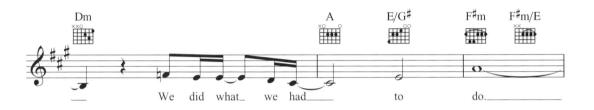

___ We did what___ we had___ to do.___

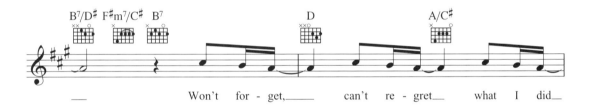

___ Won't for - get,___ can't re - gret___ what I did___

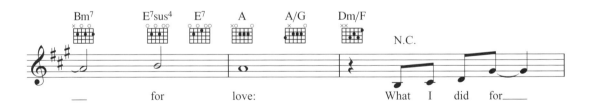

___ for love: What I did for___

rall.

love, what I did for___ love.___

Wishing You Were Somehow Here Again
(from "The Phantom Of The Opera")

Words by Charles Hart
Music by Andrew Lloyd Webber

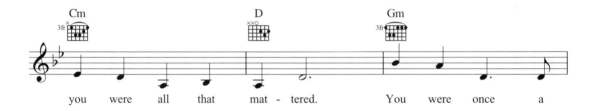

You were once my one com-pan-ion,

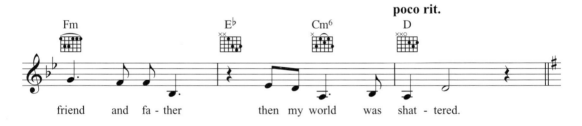

you were all that mat-tered. You were once a

friend and fa-ther then my world was shat-tered.

Wish-ing you were some-how here a-gain, wish-ing you were some-how

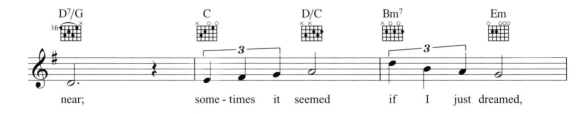

near; some-times it seemed if I just dreamed,

poco rit.   a tempo

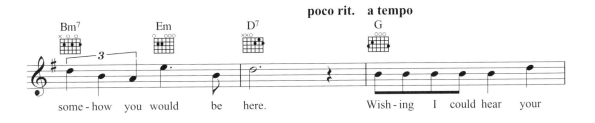

some - how you would be here.   Wish - ing I could hear your

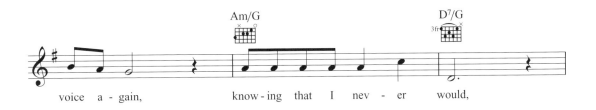

voice a - gain,   know - ing that I nev - er would,

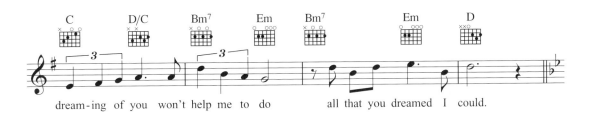

dream - ing of you won't help me to do   all that you dreamed I could.

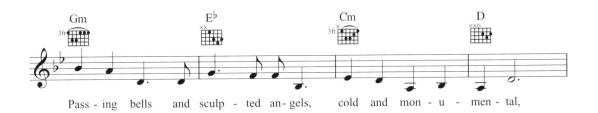

Pass - ing bells and sculp - ted an - gels,   cold and mon - u - men - tal,

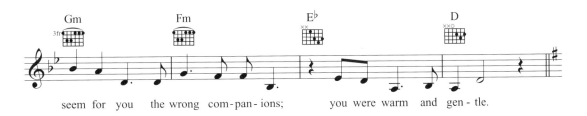

seem for you the wrong com - pan - ions;   you were warm and gen - tle.

poco meno mosso

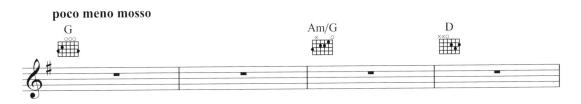

61

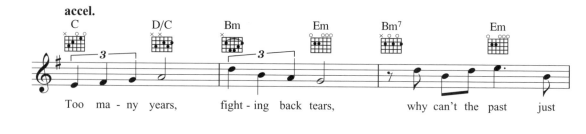

Too ma-ny years, fight-ing back tears, why can't the past just

die? Wish-ing you were some - how here a - gain,

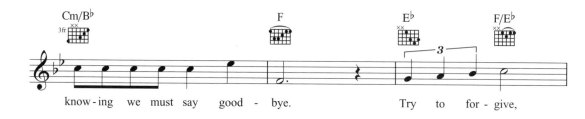

know-ing we must say good - bye. Try to for-give,

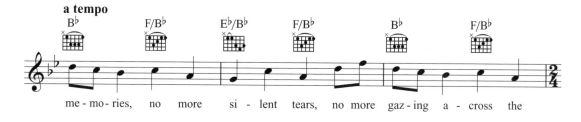

teach me to love, give me the strength to try. No more

me - mo - ries, no more si - lent tears, no more gaz-ing a - cross the

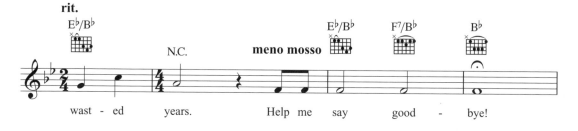

wast - ed years. Help me say good - bye!

CD Track Listing

1 As Long As He Needs Me
(Bart)
Lakeview Music Publishing Company Limited.

2 Cabaret
(Ebb/Kander)
Carlin Music Corporation.

3 Don't Cry For Me Argentina
(Rice/Lloyd Webber)
Evita Music Limited.

4 Hopelessly Devoted To You
(Farrar)
Famous Music Corporation.

5 I Don't Know How
To Love Him
(Rice/Lloyd Webber)
Universal/MCA Music Limited.

6 My Favourite Things
(Hammerstein II/Rodgers)
EMI Music Publishing Limited.

7 Memory
(Nunn/Lloyd Webber)
The Really Useful Group Limited.
Faber Music Limited.

8 Now That I've Seen Her
(Her Or Me)
(Boublil/Maltby Jr./Schönberg)
Alain Boublil (Overseas) Limited.

9 On My Own
(Boublil/Natel/Schönberg)
Alain Boublil Music Limited.

10 Shakalaka Baby
(Rahman/Black/De Vries)
The Really Useful Group Limited.

11 No One But You
(Only The Good Die Young)
(May)
EMI Music Publishing Limited.

12 Tell Me It's Not True
(Russell)
Willy Russell Music.

13 There Are Worse Things
I Could Do
(Jacobs/Casey)
Chappell Morris Limited.

14 What I Did For Love
(Kleban/Hamlisch)
Chappell Morris Limited/BMG Music Publishing Limited.

15 Wishing You Were Somehow
Here Again
(Hart/Lloyd Webber)
The Really Useful Group Limited.

To remove your CD from the plastic sleeve, lift the small lip on the right to break
the perforated flap. Replace the disc after use for convenient storage.

11/05 (56675)